# GUESS WHO?
## at the zoo

Written by Keith Faulkner
Illustrated by Jonathan Lambert

Can you help me to guess who
Lives in this house at the zoo?

When they are feeding on the trees,
They reach the highest leaves with ease.

Can you guess who it could be?
Why don't you lift the flap and see.

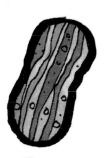
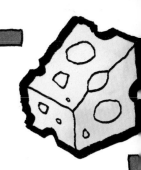

Can you help me to guess who
Lives in this house at the zoo?

It's very small and very shy.
With soft brown fur and beady eye.

Can you guess who it could be?
Why don't you lift the flap and see.

With beak and wings and colors bright,
The parrot is a wondrous sight . . .

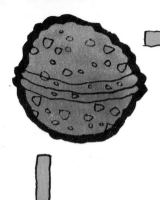

Can you help me to guess who
Lives in this house at the zoo?

They fly above the treetops high
And screech and chatter in the sky.

Can you guess who it could be?
Why don't you lift the flap and see.

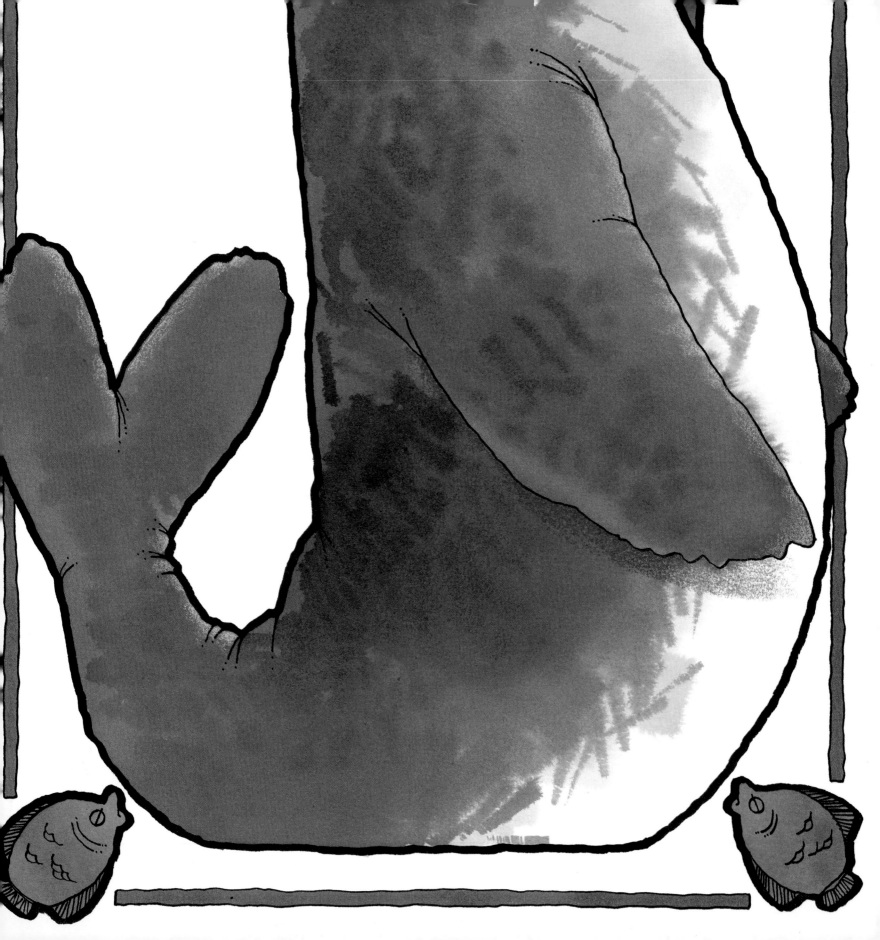

This creature knows its favorite dish,
The seal is good at catching fish . . .

Can you help me to guess who
Lives in this house at the zoo?

They live beside the salty seas.
Catching little fish with ease.

Can you guess who it could be?
Why don't you lift the flap and see.

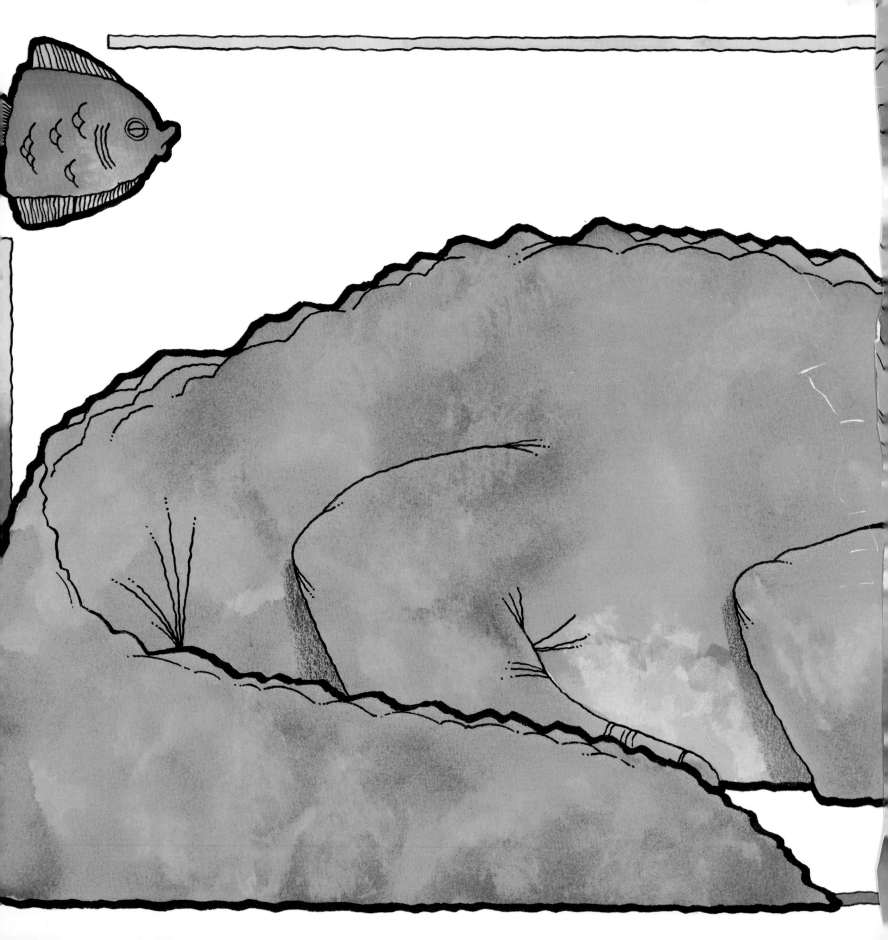

With open jaws that seem to smile,
Beware, it is a crocodile . . .

Can you help me to guess who
Lives in this house at the zoo?

They're long and green with armoured scales.
With huge sharp teeth and spiky tails.

Can you guess who it could be?
Why don't you lift the flap and see.

With wiggly trunk and flapping ears
A baby elephant appears . . .

Can you help me to guess who
Lives in this house at the zoo?

It's very big and colored gray
And likes to take a bath each day.

Can you guess who it could be?
Why don't you lift the flap and see.

With long, long legs and long neck too,
A giraffe bends down to look at you . . .

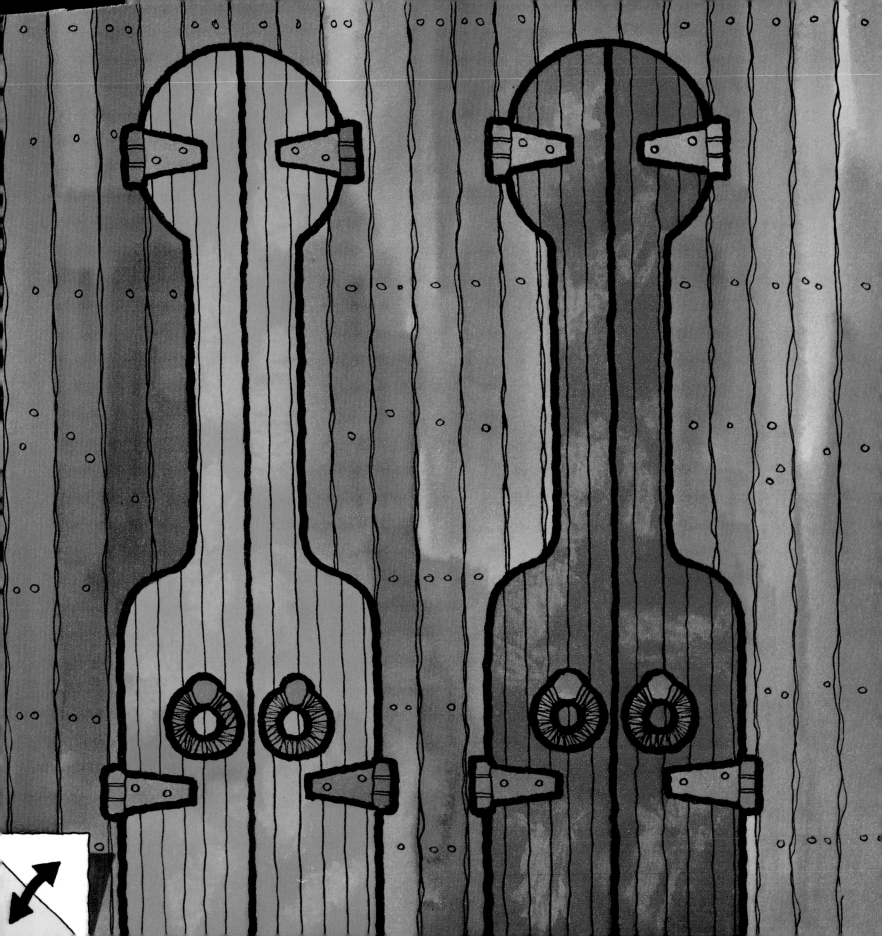